William Shakespeare

Antony and Cleopatra

First published 2015 by Walker Books Ltd
87 Vauxhall Walk, London SE11 5HJ

2 4 6 8 10 9 7 5 3 1

© 2000, 2014, 2015 Marcia Williams

The right of Marcia Williams to be identified as author/illustrator of this work
has been asserted by her in accordance with the Copyright, Designs and Patents Act 1988

This book has been typeset in Kennerly Regular

Printed and bound in China

British Library Cataloguing in Publication Data:
a catalogue record for this book is available from the British Library

ISBN 978-1-4063-6430-9

www.walker.co.uk

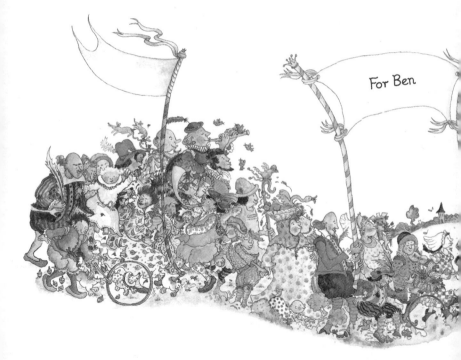

For Ben

William Shakespeare
Antony and Cleopatra

Retold by
Marcia Williams

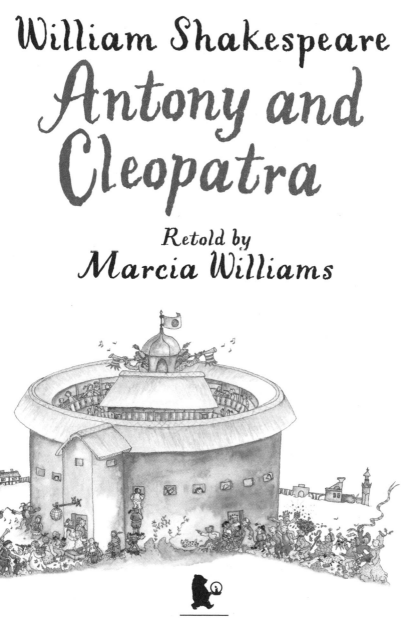

WALKER
BOOKS

Contents

In which Antony leaves Cleopatra's side.

Times were bad for the Roman world. Its borders were constantly under attack from Barbarians, and the money spent on the army to protect them had left many Romans poor and underfed. Rome was ruled by three men: Octavius Caesar, Lepidus and Mark Antony. Caesar and Lepidus did all they could to care for their country from the Senate in Rome –

but Mark Antony had vanished to Egypt.
He was there, neglecting both his country
and his wife, because of the Egyptian
queen, Cleopatra. Like Julius Caesar before
him, Antony's heart had been captured by
Cleopatra's beauty, and he could not bear
to leave her.

Most of Antony's Roman friends who
had travelled to Egypt with him found it
hard to believe that their noble general had

fallen for this gypsy queen. She treated their once proud leader like her pet dog, and still he adored her.

One day, into this Egyptian love nest came a messenger from Rome. Antony sent him away without even asking if the message was important. He seemed to have completely forgotten that he was one of Rome's leaders.

"Nay, hear them, Antony," advised

Cleopatra. "Hear the ambassadors."

"Fie, wrangling queen!" complained Antony. But eventually Antony's Roman mind overcame his Egyptian heart and he called the messenger back. The news from Rome was not good. Fulvia, his wife, had died, and his power in Rome was weakening. Caesar and Lepidus were angry with him for neglecting his duties and another general, Sextus Pompey, was trying to gain power. Antony needed to return to Rome while he still had some followers.

"I must from this enchanting queen break off," he finally decided. "Ten thousand harms, more than the ills I know, my idleness doth hatch."

Cleopatra was furious when she heard

that Antony planned to return to Rome. Even the death of Antony's wife failed to please her!

"I am sick and sullen," she said. "O, never was there queen so mightily betray'd!"

For once, Antony ignored Cleopatra's pleas, and he and his good friend Enobarbus left for Rome.

In which Roman politics comes between friends.

In Rome there was anger and fear amongst the people, for every day there were fresh uprisings and the noble Antony, whom they had once trusted and admired, was not there to guide them.

Caesar and Lepidus complained bitterly about the length of his stay in Egypt. "From Alexandria this is the news," said Caesar. "He fishes, drinks,

and wastes the lamps of night in revel."

"I must not think there are evils enough to darken all his goodness," replied the kinder Lepidus.

Lepidus found it hard to forget what a great leader Antony had once been and decided to prepare a feast to welcome him back to Rome. He hoped that the celebration would lessen Caesar's anger. It did not. From the moment Antony walked into the

room, Caesar and Antony were at each other's throats.

Yet Caesar still expressed the wish that, for the sake of Rome and for the noble Antony he had once known, he could repair their friendship somehow. Caesar's friend Agrippa suggested that Antony, who was now a widower, should marry Caesar's sister, Octavia. There was silence. Everyone looked first at Caesar, and then at Antony.

"If Cleopatra heard you...!" laughed Caesar.

Antony could not afford to think of Cleopatra at that moment, so he agreed to the plan. The two men shook hands.

"A sister I bequeath you, whom no brother did ever love so dearly," said

Caesar. "Let her live to join our kingdoms and our hearts."

Now that the three rulers were united again, they set about retrieving their strength at sea, which Pompey had usurped during Antony's long absence. They sat aboard Pompey's galley, waiting to see if he would agree to their terms.

"You have made me offer of Sicily, Sardinia, and I must rid all the sea of pirates," mused Pompey.

"That's our offer," replied the three men in unison.

"Thus we are agreed," smiled Pompey. "We'll feast each other ere we part."

So a peace treaty was signed and Antony, Lepidus and Caesar celebrated with their old friend. Many drinks later, the three leaders returned rather unsteadily to dry land.

"Give's your hand," cried Antony to Pompey as he departed.

"O, Antony!" cried Pompey, delighted to be reunited with his old friend.

Antony felt he had now done everything he could to retain his position in Rome. So he and Octavia, who was now his wife, left for Athens. They had not been there long when some terrible news reached them: Caesar had killed Pompey, imprisoned Lepidus and publicly scorned Antony!

"He hath spoke scantly of me," roared Antony, shocked and unbelieving.

"O my good lord, believe not all," cried Octavia in distress. "Or, if you must believe, stomach not all."

Octavia knew that if this was true it would mean war between her brother and husband. As she was the only person who might be able to prevent it, Octavia left for Rome at once. For the sake of speed, she chose to travel without ceremony, but her modest arrival infuriated Caesar. He felt Antony had insulted his sister.

"The wife of Antony should have an army for an usher," he ranted, stamping his foot. "But you are come a market-maid to Rome."

"To come thus was I not constrain'd, but did on my free will," promised Octavia, trying to calm her brother.

If this had been the only insult, Octavia might have succeeded in smoothing her brother's anger, but in Octavia's absence Antony had gone to visit Cleopatra in Egypt. Caesar was furious and war between the two leaders was now inevitable.

In which Cleopatra is flighty.

When Cleopatra had heard the news of Antony's marriage to Octavia she had nearly murdered the messenger in a jealous fury. Yet when Antony came back to her, she

welcomed him with open arms and he forgot his marriage in an instant. The reunited lovers decided to take up the fight against Caesar at sea, their galleys sailing together.

Enobarbus was appalled at this unwise idea. "Your ships are not well mann'd. Their ships are yare; yours, heavy," he cried.

"By sea, by sea," insisted Antony.

"Most worthy sir, you therein throw away

the absolute soldiership you have by land," insisted Enobarbus. For everyone knew Antony was almost unbeatable on land.

However, all Enobarbus's pleas were ignored. Antony only listened to Cleopatra, and she wanted him to take up the battle at sea.

"I have sixty sails, Caesar none better," said Cleopatra, ending the discussion.

Antony and Cleopatra's ships were

prepared as well as was possible with their ill-assorted crews, and the lovers left for their ships side by side. Their vessels travelled across the Ionian Sea towards Caesar's fleet. The lighter Roman ships sped swiftly to meet them. They darted amongst the Egyptian vessels like swallows amidst a herd of elephants, speckling the air with arrows and spears. Antony held firm, shouting encouragement to his beleaguered men.

Then suddenly, without any warning, Cleopatra fled from the battle with all her ships. Antony watched her go in horror – what could this mean? Why was his love deserting him? Forgetting all that was at stake he gave orders for his ship to follow her. If only he had stayed, all might have been well, but now Antony had left his fleet without a leader. Confusion followed, and although some of Antony's ships survived, most were sunk by the Romans.

As soon as Antony's feet touched dry land, he realized what he had done. He was overcome by shame. "Hark, the land bids me tread no more upon't," he wept. "It is ashamed to bear me." He had sacrificed everything for his love of Cleopatra – his honour, his power and his men. He began to feel that the only honourable course was death. "O! Whither hast thou led me, Egypt?" he raged.

"O my lord, my lord! Forgive my fearful

sails," returned Cleopatra. "I little thought you would have follow'd."

"Egypt, thou knew'st too well my heart was to thy rudder tied by the strings," Antony said bitterly.

"O! My pardon!" cried the queen, wiping away a tear.

Antony's bitterness quickly melted at the sight of Cleopatra's tears.

"Fall not a tear, I say," he cried, opening

his arms to her. "One of them rates all that is won and lost. Give me a kiss; even this repays me."

Antony and Cleopatra sent a messenger to Caesar who was encamped outside Alexandria, with terms for peace. The messenger knelt before Caesar.

"Lord of his fortunes he salutes thee and requires to live in Egypt," he said. "Next, Cleopatra does confess thy greatness,

submits her to thy might."

"For Antony, I have no ears to his
request," said Caesar coldly. He could not
forgive Antony for all that had passed.
He, his sister and Rome had been insulted
so liberally that Caesar could hardly
remember the days when he had thought
of Antony as his noble friend. He sent
word that he would make peace with
Cleopatra only if she drove Antony from
Egypt, or had him killed.

To try and encourage Cleopatra to turn against Antony, Caesar sent the message with a cunning and handsome soldier, Thyreus. Thyreus waited until Cleopatra was alone before conveying Caesar's message. "He knows that you embrace not Antony as you did love, but as you fear'd him," he said, with liquid charm.

Then, as Antony walked into the room, Thyreus took Cleopatra's hand and kissed it, lingering over it for just a moment too long.

Antony immediately suspected her of treachery. "Favours, by Jove that thunders! What art thou, fellow?" Antony yelled. "Moon and stars! Whip him."

Once more, Cleopatra soothed Antony with loving words. Still unable to resist her, his anger cooled. He decided to fight on against Caesar.

"That's my brave lord!" cried Cleopatra.

In which Cleopatra's betrayal has deadly consequences.

Much of Antony's army had already drowned or deserted him. Enobarbus had stayed loyal until this moment, but now he could see that anger and love were clouding his friend's judgement. Certain that Antony could no longer defeat Caesar, Enobarbus left to join Caesar's forces. Antony was devastated by this loss. "O, my fortunes have corrupted honest men," he groaned.

The following day, Antony went into battle with a heavy heart, little caring whether he lived or died. Yet in spite of this, the victory that day went to him, and his spirits rose. "Run one before and let the queen know," he ordered a messenger.

Cleopatra and Antony celebrated all through the night. She called him her "lord of lords" and he called her his "nightingale"! They never doubted for one

moment of that starlit night that they would soon secure the final victory.

The next morning the battle moved from land to sea, and Antony manned Cleopatra's galleys with his best troops. Antony was full of hope, and as the day wore on he seemed assured of another victory. Then, without warning, Cleopatra's boats yielded again to Caesar.

"All is lost!" roared Antony. "This foul Egyptian hath betrayed me."

This time Antony's love was totally

eclipsed by his anger. He was certain that Cleopatra had betrayed him, and he wanted her to die.

"Why is my lord enraged against his love?" appealed Cleopatra.

"Vanish, or I shall give thee thy deserving," he snarled.

Cleopatra ran from the room, calling for her maids. "Help me, my women," she called. "O, he is more than mad!"

Cleopatra took refuge in her tomb and sent word to Antony that she had killed herself.

Just as Cleopatra hoped, Antony's rage turned to despair. All was lost now – his honour, his power, his beloved Cleopatra.

"I will o'ertake thee, Cleopatra, and weep for my pardon," Antony cried.

Left without hope, Antony ordered his faithful servant, Eros, to kill him.

"Farewell, great chief. Shall I strike now?" asked Eros.

"Now, Eros," said his master.

"Why, there then; thus do I escape the sorrow..."

To avoid the pain of killing his master, Eros had fallen on his own sword.

Antony was shocked. "Thrice-nobler than myself!" he cried, and threw himself onto his own sword.

As he lay dying, a servant came from Cleopatra to say the queen still lived. Antony begged to be carried to her tomb.

Fearing Caesar's vengeful arrival, Cleopatra would not leave her tomb, so she and her maids hauled Antony over

its high walls. Then she held him lovingly in her arms.

"I am dying, Egypt, dying," he whispered. "Now my spirit is going; I can no more."

"Noblest of men, woo't die?" cried Cleopatra in panic. "Hast thou no care of me?"

It was no good. With a great cry of anguish, Cleopatra realized that Antony was dead. Wishing to die with him, she fell to the ground.

In which an unusual suicide is committed.

When Caesar heard that Antony was dead, he was determined to capture Cleopatra alive as a symbol of his victory. He sent one of his officers, Proculeius, to Cleopatra's

tomb to prevent the queen from dying along with her lover.

"Her life in Rome would be eternal in our triumph," declared Caesar, almost jumping with delight at the thought.

Proculeius entered the tomb just in time to stop Cleopatra from stabbing herself.

"Where art thou, death? Come hither, come!" screamed Cleopatra, furious that Proculeius had prevented her death. Then Caesar himself arrived.

"Our care and pity is so much upon you, that we remain your friend," he promised.

But Cleopatra knew he was secretly plotting to parade her as his prisoner through Rome. She had to act quickly or he would succeed – Caesar was already preparing to return to Rome and Cleopatra was to be sent before him.

First Cleopatra ordered her maids, Charmian and Iras, to fetch her finest robes. "Show me, my women, like a queen,"

she ordered. "Bring our crown and all."

Then she asked them to call for a farmer to deliver a basket of figs.

"Hast thou the pretty worm of Nilus there?" she asked him when he arrived.

"Truly, I have him," answered the farmer, looking in awe at Egypt's magnificent queen. "But I would not be the party that should desire you to touch him, for his biting is immortal."

Cleopatra waved his worries aside.

Once her maids had helped her to dress in all her finery, the queen opened the basket. There, nestled amongst the figs, lay two poisonous asps. Cleopatra lifted them gently, putting one serpent to her breast and one to her arm.

"Dost thou not see my baby at my breast that sucks the nurse asleep?" she said.

"O, break! O, break!" Charmian cried out in distress.

But it was too late. As the asps delivered their venom, Cleopatra thought of Antony. "O Antony!" she whispered, as though with her dying breath she fell into his arms.

By their deaths, Antony and Cleopatra had robbed Caesar of his triumph. Yet Antony had once been the noblest of Roman generals, and in spite of all their quarrels, Caesar mourned for him. He gave orders that the bodies of Charmian and Iras,

who had poisoned themselves, be removed
from the monument. Then his army attended
Antony and Cleopatra's funeral with full

solemnity, placing the two lovers together in the queen's tomb so they would stay in death as they had in life, side by side.

WILLIAM SHAKESPEARE was a popular playwright, poet and actor who lived in Elizabethan England. He married in Stratford-upon-Avon aged eighteen and had three children, although one died in childhood. Shakespeare then moved to London, where he wrote 39 plays and over 150 sonnets, many of which are still very popular today. In fact, his plays are performed more often than those of any other playwright, and he died 450 years ago! His gravestone includes a curse against interfering with his burial place, possibly to

deter people from opening it in search of unpublished manuscripts. It reads, "Blessed be the man that spares these stones, and cursed be he that moves my bones." Spooky!

MARCIA WILLIAMS' mother was a novelist and her father a playwright, so it's not surprising that Marcia ended up an author herself. Although she never trained formally as an artist, she found that motherhood, and the time she spent later as a nursery school teacher, inspired her to start writing and illustrating children's books.

Marcia's books bring to life some of the world's all-time favourite stories and some colourful historical characters. Her hilarious retellings and clever observations will have children laughing out loud and coming back for more!

More retellings from Marcia Williams

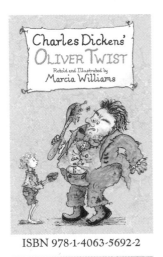

ISBN 978-1-4063-5692-2

ISBN 978-1-4063-5693-9

ISBN 978-1-4063-5694-6

ISBN 978-1-4063-5695-3

Available from all good booksellers

www.walker.co.uk